Sources of Inspiration:

Collage comes from the French word "colle," meaning glue. Artists Pablo Picasso and Georges Braque are credited with coining the term "collage" in 1913. These artists, along with Henri Matisse, were some of the first to bring collage into their art. In this story, Henri is loosely based on Henri Matisse, who was well-known for his colorful studio and huge, cut-paper collages.

COLLETTE A Collage Adventure

PRT1113A

Printed in the United States.

Library of Congress Control Number: 2013950821

ISBN-13: 9781620864579
ISBN-10: 1620864576

www.mascotbooks.com

Collette
A Collage Adventure
Kathryn Horn Coneway
Kathryn Horn Coneway

A small bottle of glue lived on a shelf in Henri's art studio.
Her name was Collette.

Collette's spot on the shelf offered a wonderful
view of the bright and colorful workshop.

Every day, Collette watched as Henri painted big strokes of color. The paints formed lines and shapes, and a painting was born. It was always a surprise - sometimes even to Henri!

In the evening, Henri wrote to artists and friends all over the world. Collette sat on the desk as he glued stamps and labels onto letters.

Sometimes, Henri's friends visited.

Collette loved to hear them talk about colors. They spoke of the fiery reds, energetic oranges, and calm blues as if they were friends, too.

Collette wished for a way to join the conversation.

COLLE

One day, Henri's neighbor, Jeanette, peeked through the doorway. "Come in, Jeanette!" he said.

She looked all around at the paintings and bright colors. Then, she saw Collette. "What is this paint for?" she asked. "I like her name."

Henri laughed. "That's my glue. The label says 'colle.' With this scrap of paper stuck on, it says 'Collette.' Collette and Jeanette – you two could be quite a pair!"

Jeanette put Collette down gently and began to explore Henri's desk. She found a scrapbook filled with photographs, postcards, and drawings.

"I have lots of pictures and drawings at home. Could I make a book like this?"

"Of course!" said Henri. "And my friend Collette can help you!"

POLSKA
zł
1,00

The next day, Henri gave Jeanette a book of her own.
She sat down to work with Collette.

It didn't go too well.

Sometimes, Jeanette didn't use enough glue and her pictures wouldn't stay.

Other times, Jeanette used too much glue and the pages of her book became soggy and wet.

Poor Collette ended up all sticky and covered in torn bits of paper!

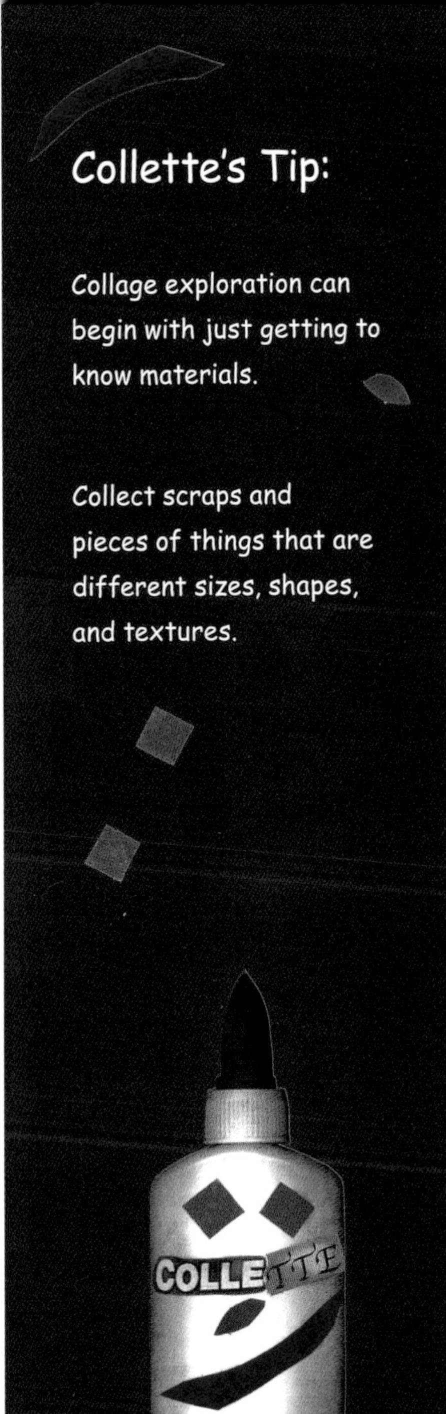

Collette's Tip:

Collage exploration can begin with just getting to know materials.

Collect scraps and pieces of things that are different sizes, shapes, and textures.

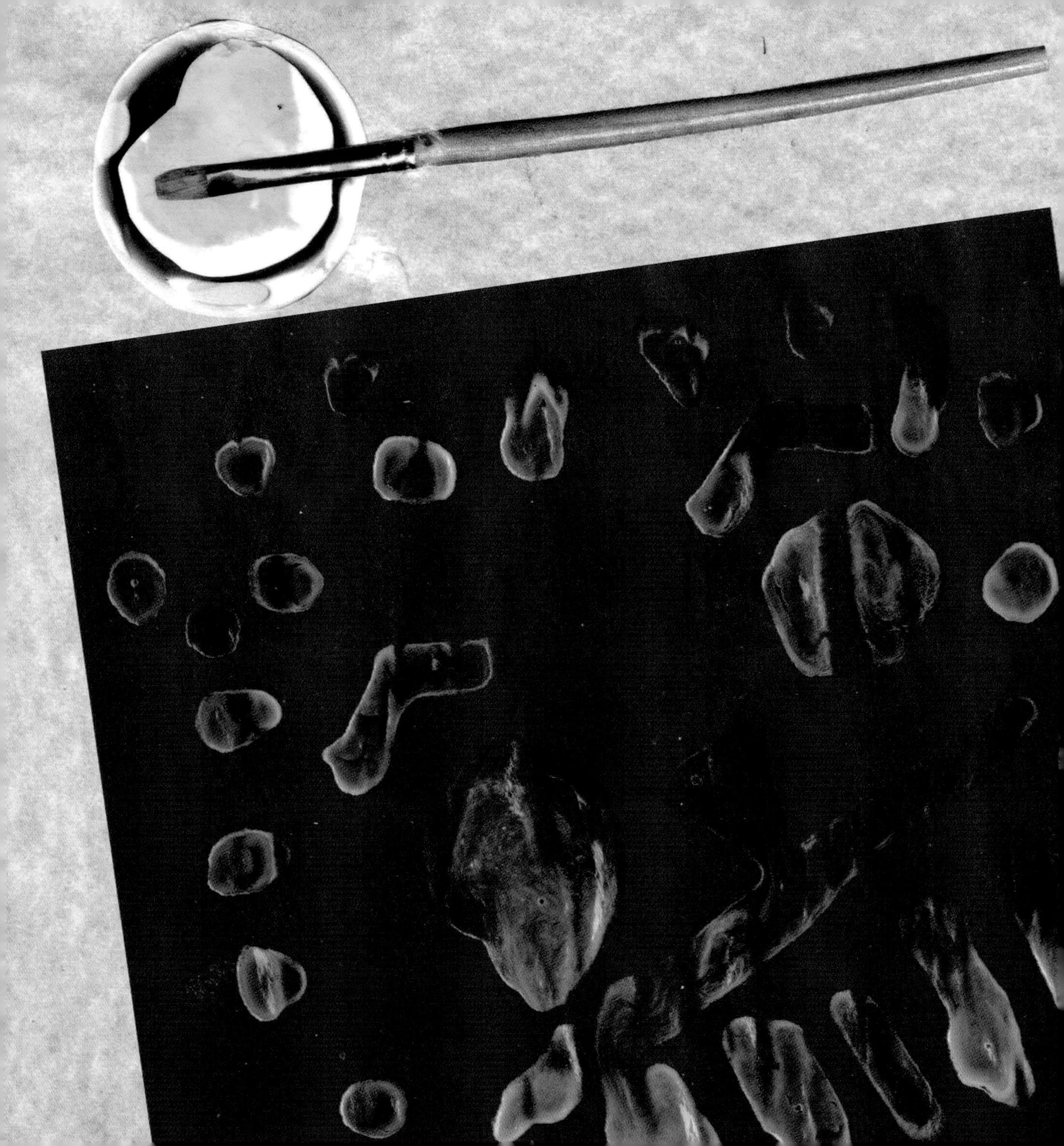

Henri suggested Jeanette paint the glue onto her pictures to stick them to the page.

Her pasting went better after that. When she finished, Jeanette turned to a new page and began to paint with the glue.

Aha! thought Collette. *With a brush, I can be just like Henri's beautiful paint.*

As the glue dried, however, it became transparent and the lines and shapes nearly vanished.

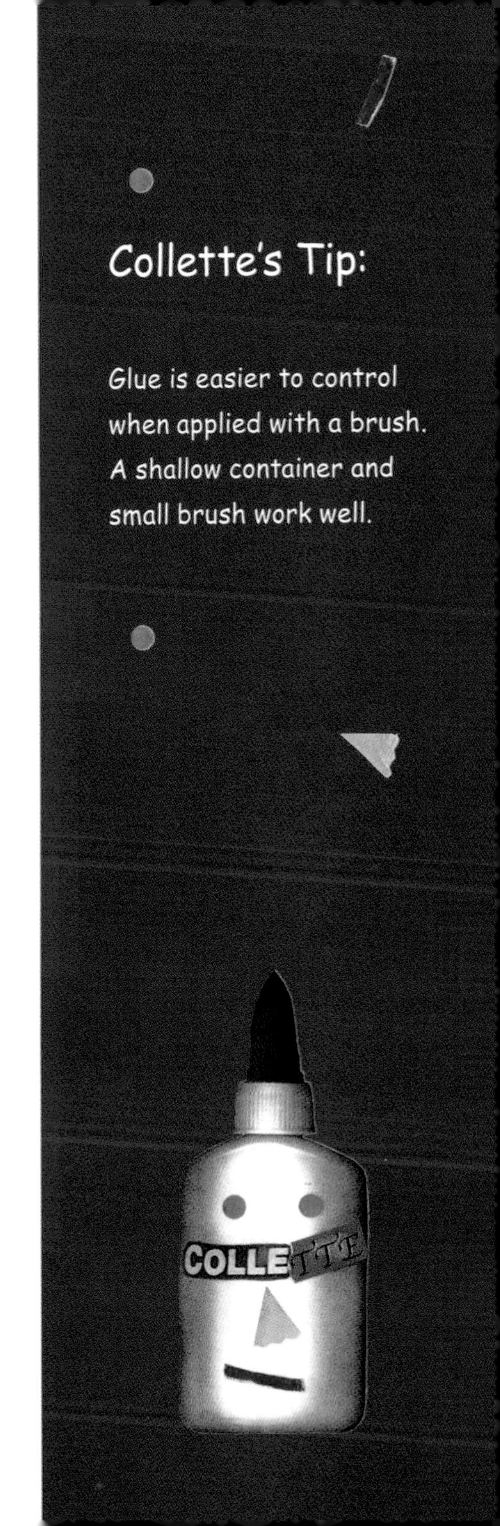

Collette's Tip:

Collage is a great way to recycle artistic explorations and abandoned art projects.

Cut pieces from crayon rubbings, drawings, or colorful painted papers.

Henri ran his fingers over the clear glue. "There are some wonderful shapes here. Let's see what we can do."

Henri placed a piece of white paper over the clear glue shapes. He rubbed with the side of a red crayon. Like magic, the shapes appeared on the paper!

He showed Jeanette how to do the same thing with a leaf. For the rest of the afternoon, Collette watched as Jeanette made crayon rubbings.

The next morning, Jeanette returned with a collection of materials for more rubbings. She set them out on the paper.

Collette was sad she couldn't be part of the fun. Then, she had an idea.

Collette spilled onto the paper. There was glue everywhere!

"It's ruined!" cried Jeanette.

Jeanette looked at the mess and wondered what to do. Sadly, she moved a button around in the glue. She pushed it next to a ribbon and left it. Next, she slid another button across the page. She began adding pieces. Suddenly, a trio of acrobats appeared.

"Collette!" exclaimed Jeanette. "Look what we can do!"

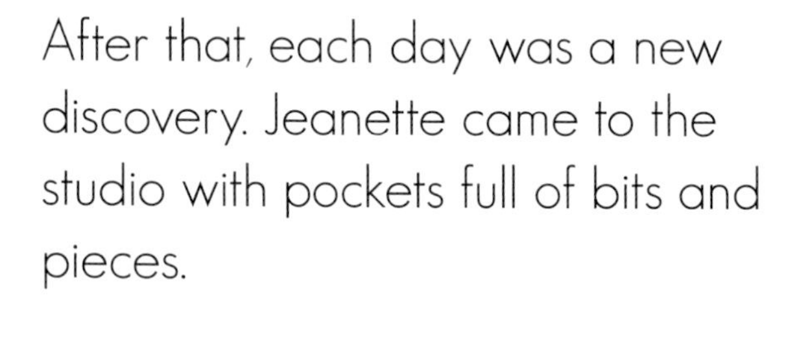

After that, each day was a new discovery. Jeanette came to the studio with pockets full of bits and pieces.

One day, she played with a piece of string until it formed a tree.

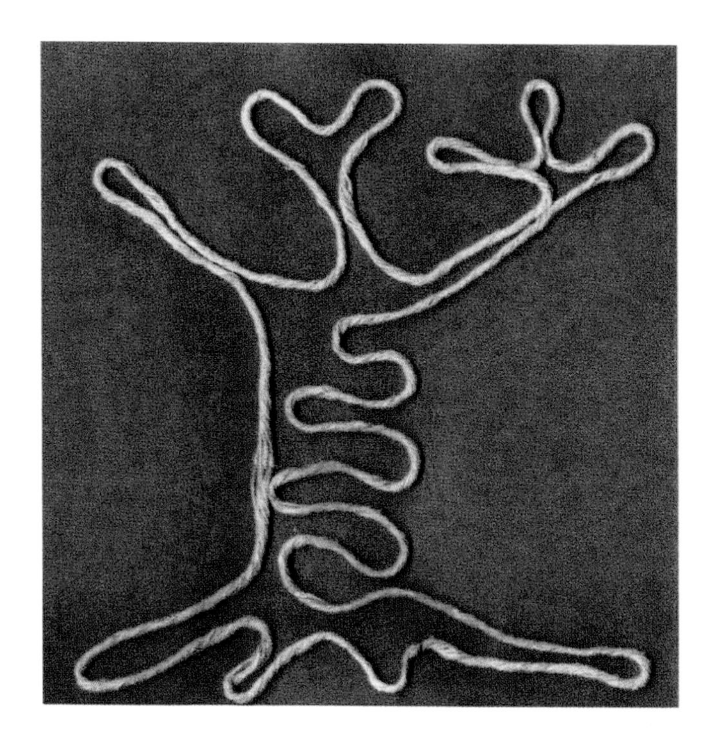

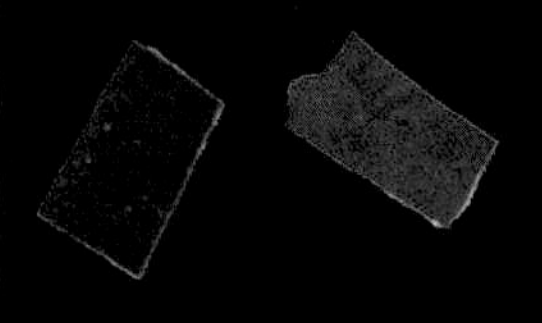

Collette's Tip:

Working in layers can add dimension and texture to your work.

Tissue paper and other translucent materials allow pieces to show through.

The wind blew and Collette became covered in scraps of tissue paper. Jeanette saw the bright colors and used the scraps to shape bark and leaves for the tree.

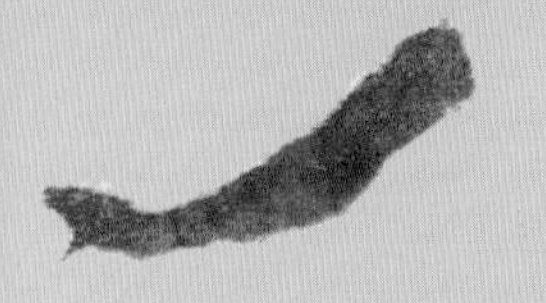

Collette's Tip:

Faces are a great theme for collage exploration. Notice how different shapes and arrangements suggest different emotions.

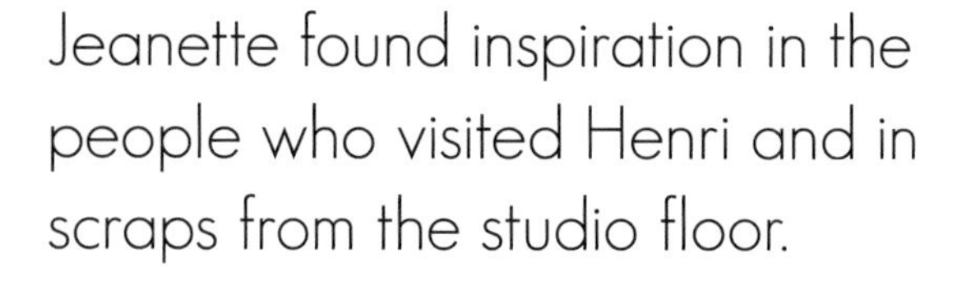

Jeanette found inspiration in the people who visited Henri and in scraps from the studio floor.

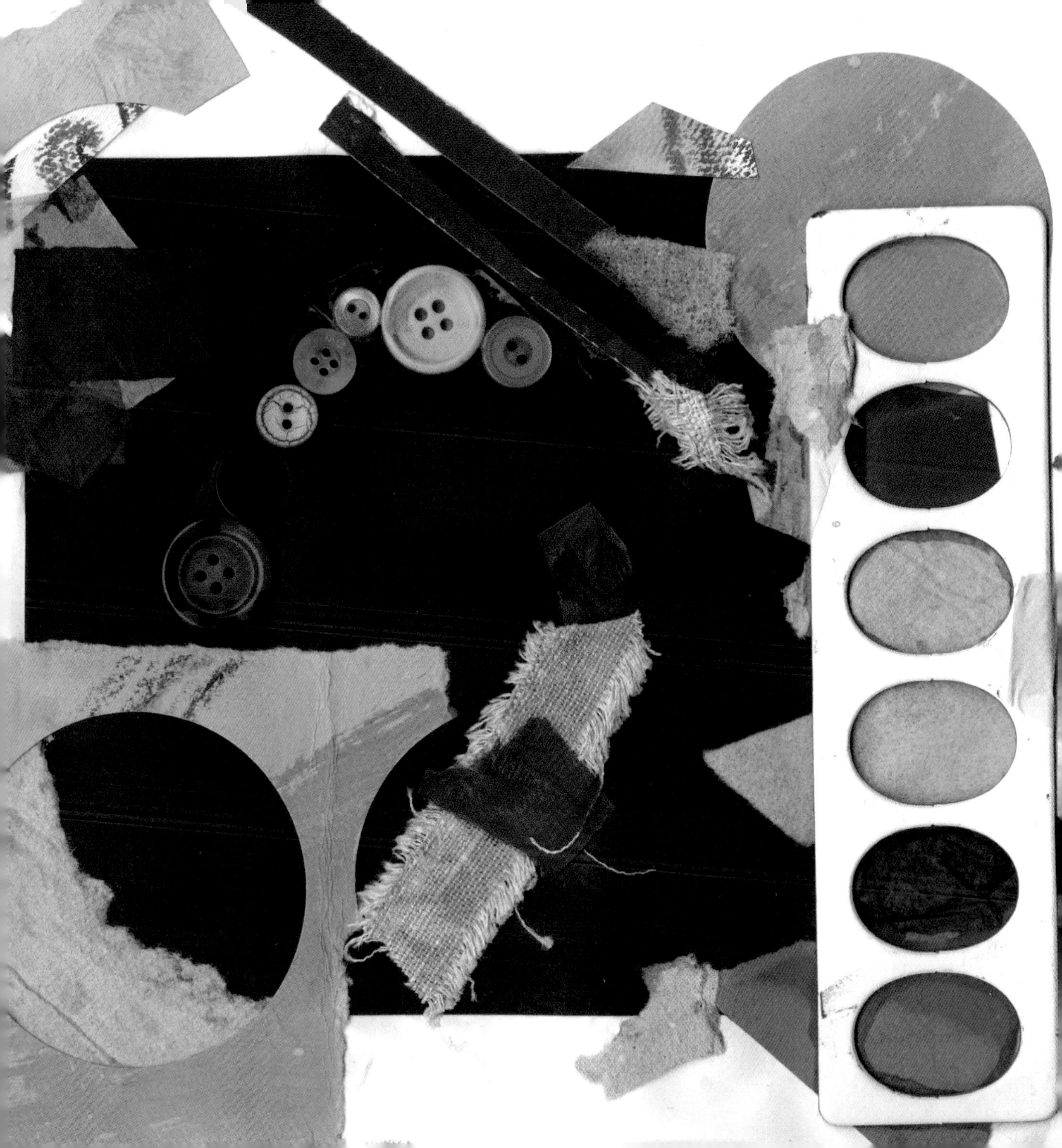

Collette's Tip:

Abstract collages provide opportunities for talking about line, shape, and color.

Have fun turning your collage to look for hidden images.

Sometimes, looking at their pictures was like looking at shapes in the clouds.

Where Jeanette saw a bird in a tree, Collette saw a woman with a red dress and wild hair.

One day, the picture would grow on its own – a tangled jungle of found pieces.

On another day, a scrap would suggest the shape of something familiar.

Things they noticed became subjects for collages – the view out the window…

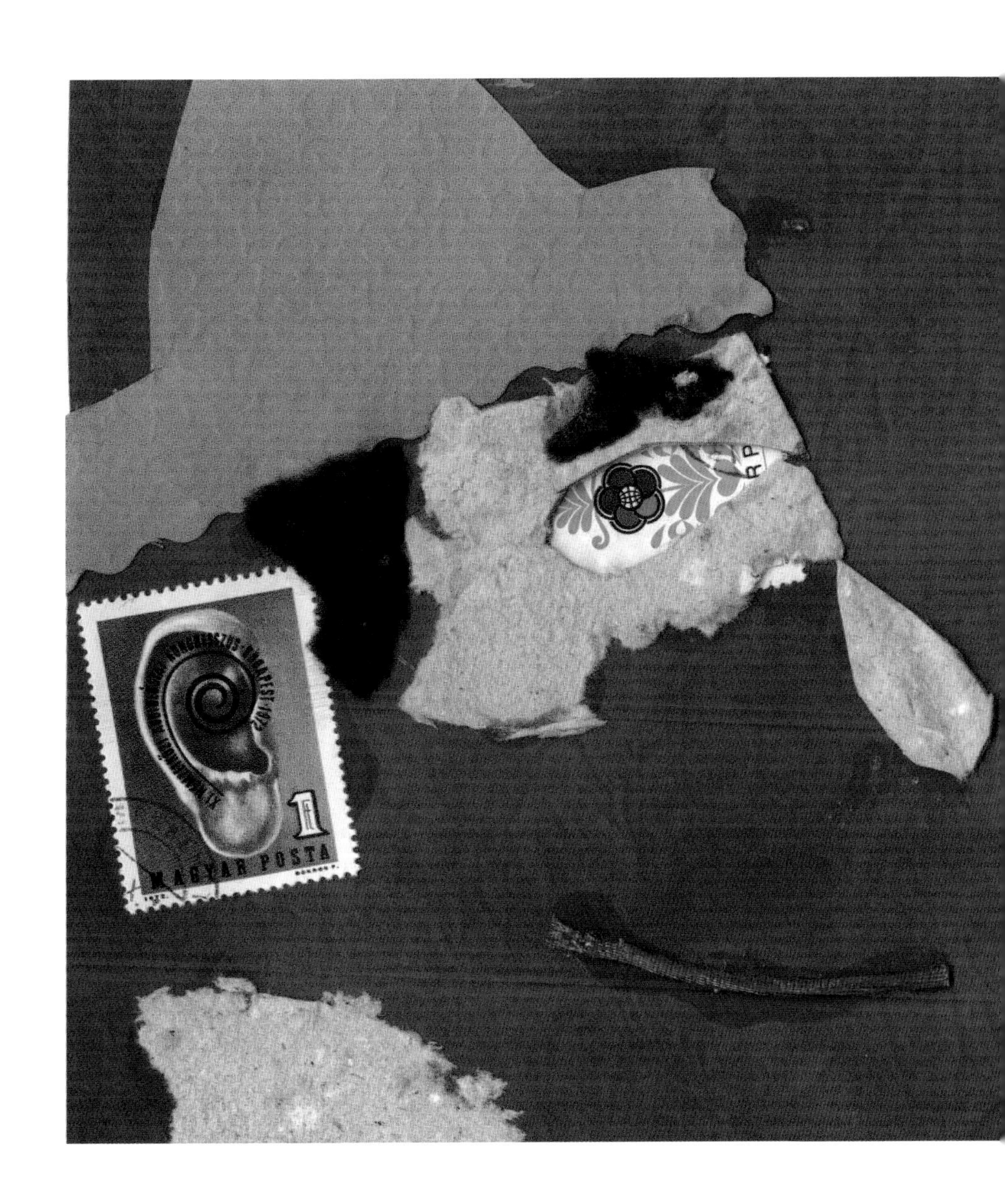

...and Henri's
shy smile.

Torn bits of paper suggested leaves
or snow.

Squares and rectangles created buildings.

Henri and his friends, Pablo and Georges, were inspired. They began gluing pieces to paintings too. They called this form of art "collage."

Collette was thrilled to finally be part of the art.

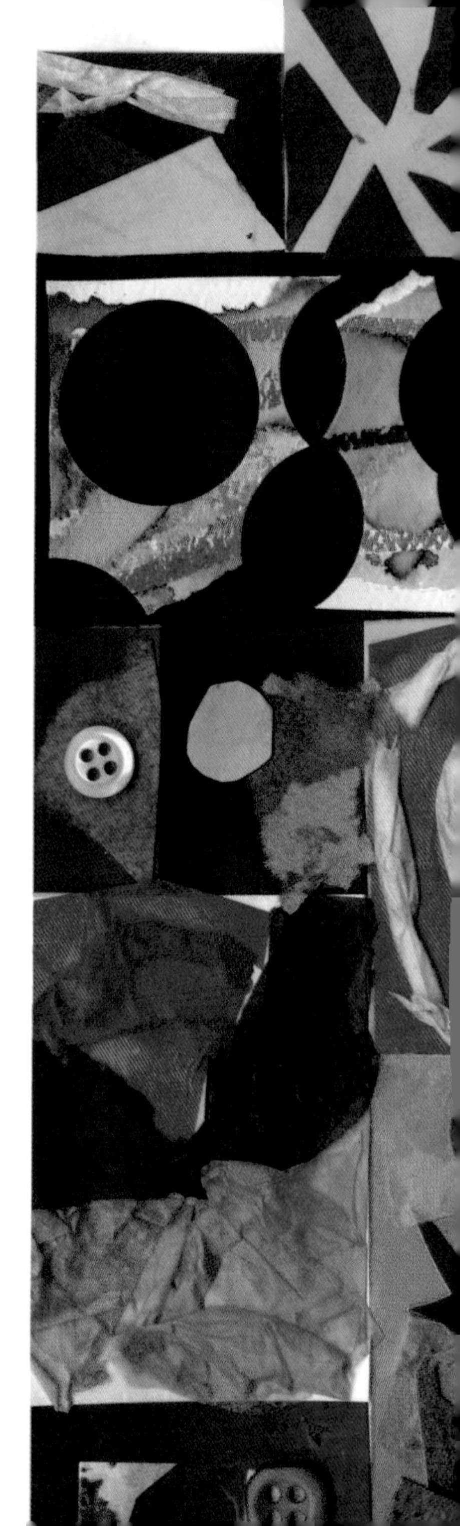

COLLE

Imagine what you and Collette can create together!

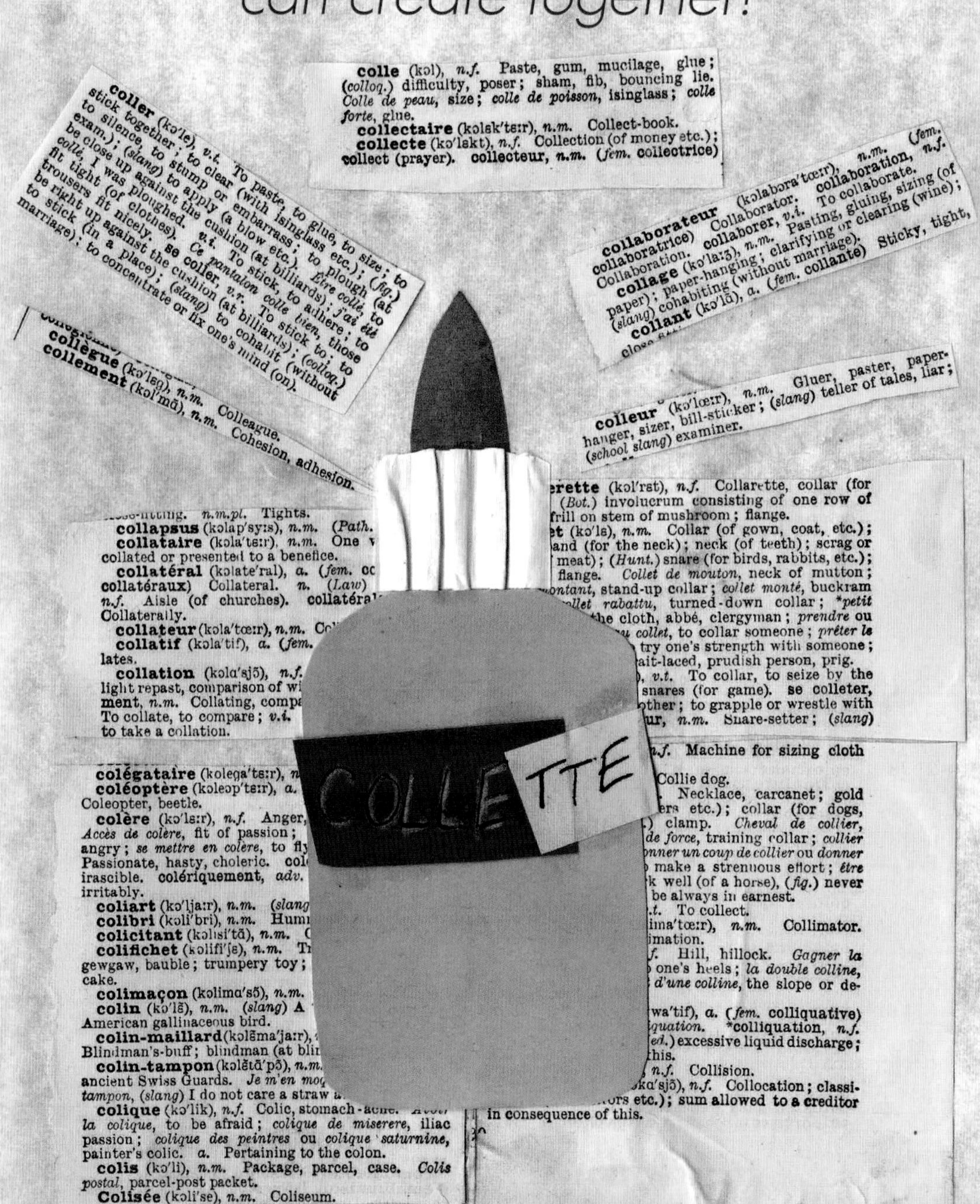

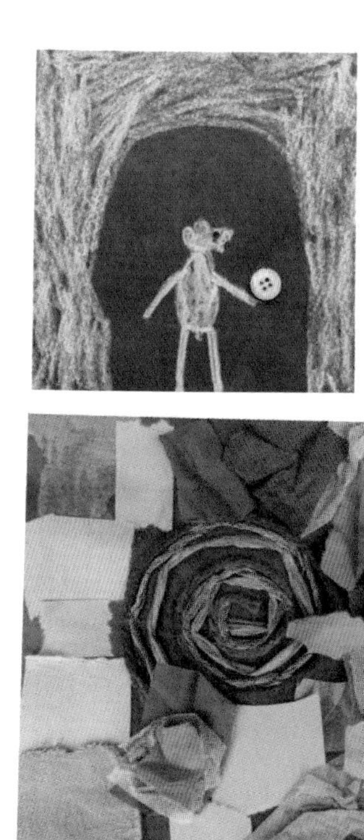
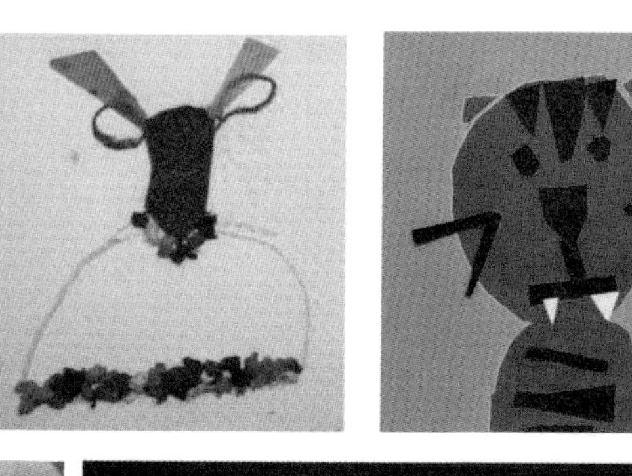

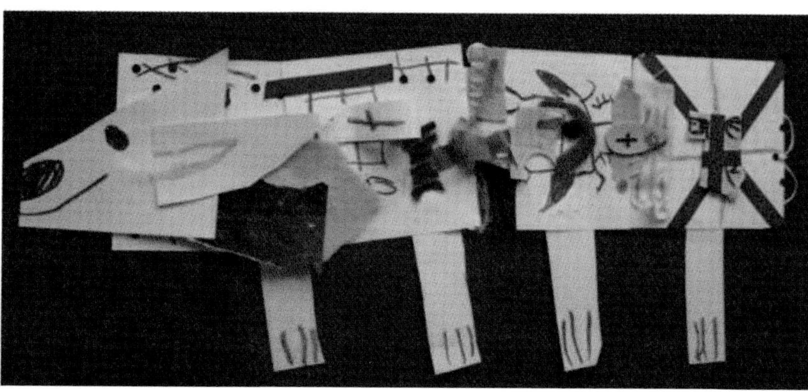

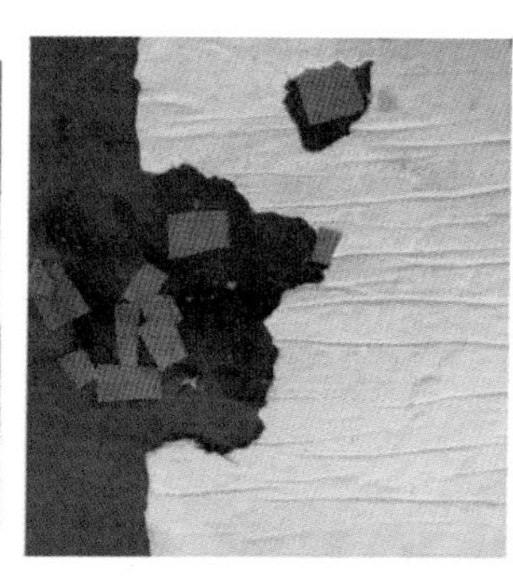

A note for parents, teachers, and other collage companions...

Collage exploration often begins with a fascination with glue and the way it spreads, oozes, and drips. A drop of watercolor or food coloring in the glue will help make glue marks more visible.

Collage is a good introductory art project because it can begin with simple play with materials. Young artists can move from exploring shapes and textures to forming designs and then images.

Designing with materials complements children's natural tendency to collect bits and pieces. Begin a collection of found materials at home and practice sorting and arranging your found pieces.

I find it helpful to return to collage as a theme, offering slightly different materials to create a new focus. One time we'll use torn paper, another time cut shapes, and still another transparent pieces or combinations of these. Black and white, warm and cool colors, and different textures make other good collage variations.

Collage is a great way to model being open to the process and to "happy accidents." Look for ways to see mistakes or surprises as opportunities for transformation and growth. Join your child in exploring collage. Sharing is a vital part of the creative journey.

Thank you for allowing me to share this story with you. I would love to hear your story, too.

Please email Collette@artatthecenter.org to share your collage adventures!

-Kathryn